"Seven pounds, three ounces—seven pounds,
three ounces—seven pounds. . . . "

Many
Happy Returns

"Through here."

Many
Happy Returns

By

Ted Key
Creator of "Hazel"

E. P. Dutton & Co., Inc.
New York · 1951

Acknowledgment

The drawings in this volume appeared originally in *The Saturday Evening Post, This Week, Colliers, Ladies Home Journal, The Philadelphia Inquirer, Better Homes and Gardens, The American Magazine, Cosmopolitan.*

The artist and the publisher wish to express their gratitude to the editors of these publications for permission to reproduce them here.

Individual Copyrights

The individual cartoons have been previously published and Copyright as follows:

By The Curtis Publishing Company in *The Saturday Evening Post*: 1943, P. 19, 78; 1944, P. 55, 56; 1946, P. 44; 1947, P. 36, 38, 40, 43, 50, 53, 62, 63, 67, 77, 84, 88, 89; 1948, P. 18, 25, 27, 28, 29, 32, 33, 34, 36, 38, 40, 46, 56, 59, 60, 62, 66, 69, 78, 79; 1949, P. 4, 9, 11, 12, 13, 16, 19, 21, 22, 26, 30, 32, 35, 39, 44, 45, 46, 51, 52, 58, 66, 68, 69, 70, 73, 76, 83, 85; 1950, P. 6, 14, 15, 17, 20, 22, 23, 24, 28, 31, 34, 39, 42, 47, 52, 53, 60, 61, 64, 65, 71, 72, 80, 81, 82, 89, 91; 1951, P. 93.

By The Curtis Publishing Company in *Ladies Home Journal*: 1948, P. 77; 1949, P. 47, 63; 1950, P. 67.

By The *Philadelphia Inquirer*: 1948, P. 16, 18; 1949, P. 25, 29, 54, 79, 82, 83 and endpapers.

By Crowell-Collier in *The American Magazine*: 1950, P. 91.

By United Newspapers Magazine Corp., in *This Week*: 1947, P. 71; 1948, P. 72; 1949, P. 37, 86, 87; 1950, P. 50, 74, 75.

By Meredith Publishing Co., in *Better Homes and Gardens*: 1948, P. 70; 1950, P. 58, 59, 87.

By Hearst Magazines, Inc. in *Cosmopolitan*: 1950, P. 20, 90.

By Crowell-Collier in *Colliers*: 1947, P. 23, 43; 1949, P. 57, 90; 1950, P. 41; 1951, P. 92.

TO STEPHEN AND DAVID

"To continue . . ."

"Murch's chicken coop."

1   "Everything he touches seems to grow."

2

3

Green

6

7

4

5

Thumb

9

"When I say dinner!"

"That's all very well, and suppose she's NOT sitting on your jeep."

"Neck too."

"So . . . they don't take boys with bad eyes!?"

"Spoke to S. H. about it, Joe. He thinks K. S. oughta team up with B.F.
or J. B. Now, what I called you about—who's K. S., B. F. and J. B.?"

"I'll let you guys in on a little secret. You know why they let you eat so much around here?"

"What cost seven cents?"

"And write often. You know how wor-
ried I get, Henry—I mean George."

"Better get used to it — won't be her last caller."

THE SUITOR

"UNDERSTAND YOU'RE A SALESMAN?"

"So the bus can't seat eight, eh?"

1

"Jones!"

2

"With mustard!"

"Netting us a neat . . . you listening? . . . forty per cent . . ."

1

"My name is Harding, Ted Harding. Got a charge account with you. Last month we bought one of your new toasters and it didn't work. Well, today we received your bill and... transfer me to Electrical Appliances? Certainly."

2

"My name is Harding. Harding. H-A-R-D-I-N-G. Bought a toaster from you last month which didn't work. Naturally we sent it back, but today, when we got your bill . . . Complaint Department? Okay."

3

"Name's Harding. Bought a toaster which didn't work so we sent it back. Today you sent us a bill . . . Credit Department?"

4

"Harding, bought a toaster. Didn't work. Sent it back. Got a bill. What? Adjustment?"

5

"No—a toaster! Yes—a bill! Who? The Complaint Department!!!?"

6

". . . toaster toaster toaster toaster toaster toaster toaster . . ."

"Dear . . ."

". . . about 2500 B. C., during—during—the early
—the early Sumerian—Sumerian dynasties . . ."

"Not that we do *everything* the book says, but we feel . . ."

"Doesn't look appetizing—I'll have . . ."

"It's been *SO* nice."

"Our boy."

"Wouldn't have the man on my payroll."

"MO-THER!"

"MO-THER!"

"I'm home."

". . . or $20,000 for the loss of TWO limbs and ONE eye. Now here's where you're going to THANK me. Suppose you're killed outright . . ."

"Is your mother . . . ?"

"... but just then the bear ..."

"THE BEAR WHAT?"

"The bear ..."

"Look, suppose we let Ellie do it her own way."

"Look, dear, if you want me to, I can move the
kittens from your closet and put them . . ."

"Oh, thought it might be . . ."

"What kept you?"

"He's in the gang."

THE
SHY ONE

1 " 'The Village Blacksmith,' by Henry Wadsworth Longfellow"

2

3 "Under . . ."

4

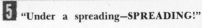

5 "Under a spreading—SPREADING!"

6

7

8

"Under a spreading chestnut tree
   The village smithy stands;
The smith, a mighty man is he,
   With large and sinewy hands;
And the muscles of his brawny arms
   Are strong as iron bands.
His hair is crisp, and black, and long . . ."

"Well, folks, they're on the one-yard line
and what an exciting moment this is!"

"MENU!"

"How long are you going to sit there?!"

"Here's another taken when he was four."

"Woman driver!"

"I dunno where the boys in the shipping
department got the idea you're stuffy . . ."

"How do you apply a tourniquet?"

"Well—he bled to death. Now, how do you . . ."

"If you think for one minute that I'm going to stay cooped up in that house, cooking your meals and washing your clothes and raising your children while you . . .!"

"All set?"

"Passing through a phase."

"And your beef—I mean problem?"

"... well, sort of busy ... ho, you silly boy, you ... tonight? Oh, I couldn't ... you flatterer ... well ... I know I shouldn't ... ask me nicely ... pretty please ... with sugar on it ..."

"How's Yale?"

"Short cut?"

"Shall we save the cost of living till after the dessert?"

"I know this; if it weren't for him, and men like him, we wouldn't <u>have</u> a volunteer fire department."

". . . the water in the percolator. Then you take your coffee, regular grind . . ."

1

"Consolidated
Industries
Incorporated,
good morning."

"This is
Mintcolm J. Poomp.
May I speak to
Mr. Gook, please?"

2

"May I
speak to
Mr. Gook,
please?"

"Executive
Planning
and
Distribution."

WHO
SHALL
I SAY
IS CALLING?

3

"Sectional
Overhaul
and Sub-
contracting."

"Mr. Gook, please."

4

"Mr. Gook!"

"Knickknacks,
Replacements."

Sub-discards
and Waste."

"MR. GOOK!"

6

"Poomp? Sorry, Mr. Poomp, but Mr. Gook seems to be . . ."

"I also ordered buttered toast."

"One thing we <u>never</u> do in the Fire Department . . ."

1

"Behind twenty-four to twelve.
Then they shot six baskets . . ."

"But not knowing the account
was overdrawn, we naturally
went ahead and..."

2

"*YOU* went ahead . . ."

3

"...and scored twelve..."

"*I* went ahead and made
out these checks and..."

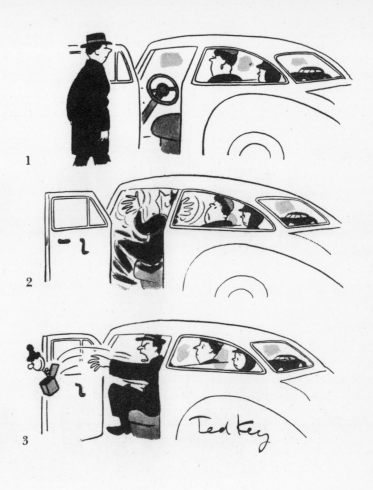

1

2

3

"Veal cutlet."

CUFF LINKS

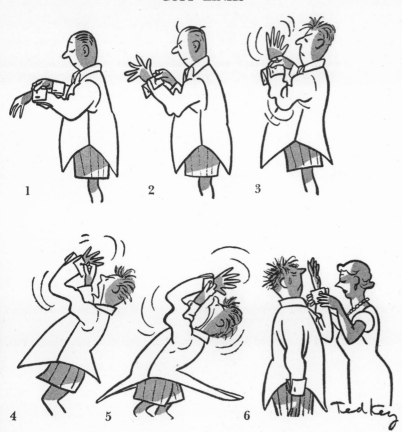

1

"And so, without further ado, I give you Mr. Roger Ecklin Stoop, the founder and the chairman of our company, without whose . . . without whose . . ."

2

". . . patience, foresight and intelligence. . . ."

3

"Whew . . . almost passed that stop sign!"

"Quitting?"

"Can't do a thing with it!"

"You can step out now, Sweet."

"... Foreclosing our mortgage. Haven't told Lil yet. The wife. She's been in the hospital over a year. Talk about bills! Sister's takin' care of the kids. Her husband run off, y'know—just up an' left, just like that. With business the way it is ..."

"Keep the change"

"... Foreclosing our mortgage, Haven't told Lil yet. The wife. She's been in the hospital over a year. Talk about bills! ..."

GROWTH CHART

One year   Five   Ten   Fifteen   Twenty

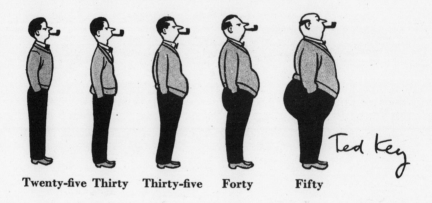

Ted Key

Twenty-five   Thirty   Thirty-five   Forty   Fifty

Favorite child

Love graph

THE URGE

THE AGE

UNMARRIED

1

2

"Why, darling, you didn't
tell me you could sing!"

MARRIED

3

4

"Not that I object person-
ally, but the neighbors..."

"I trust everything was . . ."

"Helen, Emily, Dorothy, Angelica, Frances, Constance, Violet, Mary, Katherine, Lily, Susan, Nancy, Anne, Edith, Flora, Inez, Alice, Mildred, Gloria, Pauline, Marione, Lucy, Judith, Charlotte, Agnes, Deborah, Robin, Georgiana, Elizabeth, Caroline, Priscilla, Louise, Phillis, Josephine, Margaret . . ."

"... I says to her and she says to me
and I says to her and she says to..."

"Well,—when the driver *does* come, will you tell him that the slacks I *thought* needed cleaning . . ."

"Well, well, look who the cat drag—*LOOK WHO'S HERE!*"

"Tell them to start passing, get Tubby closer
to that line and pull up Billie's pants."

"Robberies, shootings, stabbings—you
should have the children for a day!"

THE
MARRIAGE
EXPERT

1. "After all, marriage is a partnership. Give and take. If your wife could participate in more of your activities, could share in your . . ."

2.   "Bait's gone."

5.   "Cute uniforms."

6.

Ted Kerz

3. ". . . wearing last year's organdy, only dyed a ghastly purple, with the hem taken . . ."

4. "Listen to this name!"

7. "KILL HIM!"

8. "First, of course, we must get your husband back . . ."

"You young folks! Where you get the
notion that a man who's sixty . . ."

"What time did the office party start?"

"This is the story of Jack and the Beanstalk. Once upon a time—once upon a time—once upon a time—once upon a time—once upon a time . . ."

"He's real cute, Mr. Stuart. He looks just like your wife."

"... to the left a little. Too much. Over. Over. Wee
bit more. Now back. A little more. Wee bit. That's
just about—that's it. Perfect. Now hold it. Hold . . ."

1

2

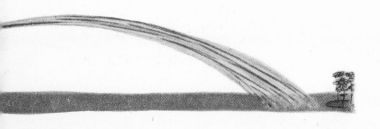

"Now let's see—Willy bid one spade. Mr. Baker passed, I bid two hearts, Mrs. Baker passed, Willy bid three spades, Mr. Baker passed, I bid four clubs, Mrs. Baker passed, Willy bid four spades, Mr. Baker passed, I bid five diamonds, Mrs. Baker passed, Will bid five spades, Mr. Baker passed—and now it's up to me. Excuse me while I sort these cards . . ."

"Happy birthday to you—
Happy birthday to you—
Happy birthday, dear Eustace . . ."

"Well, kid, you saw a show,
you had a hamburger . . ."

"Someone better take these nuts away from me."

"Fork"

1

You give her years of piano lessons . . .

2

And five years of the dance . . .

3

Handpick her schools . . .

4

Introduce culture . . .

Broaden her horizons . . .

6

Spend oodles for clothes . . .

Have her meet the right people . . .

8

So what happens?

"Think of it as an investment . . ."

"You'll always have a home, darling."

"Use the triangle fold myself."

". . . the jungle's magic potion began to work.
He felt *younger*, mysteriously *stronger*. Sud-
denly—AYEEEYAH! He glanced at his mate——"

FAMILY TREE

"Okay, Mom—start backing."

SUNDAY
RIDE

by
Ted Key

1. "All set?"
   "Lock the screen door?"

2. "Screen door's locked."

3. "All set?"
   "Cat in or out?"

4. "Cat's out."

5. "All set?"
   "Close all the windows?"

6. "Windows closed."

7. "ALL SET?"

8.

9. "All set?"

10.

"Cut the meat balls in half?"

1

"She got *in*, didn't she?"

2

"... yes, you. Would you kindly sit down so our camera can ..."

"Well—time for that ol' phone call."

"Well, let's see. I get off at eight. My husband
picks me up. We put the children to bed. I read
the paper—talk a bit—bathe—go to bed. Why?"

THE SHOWER BATH

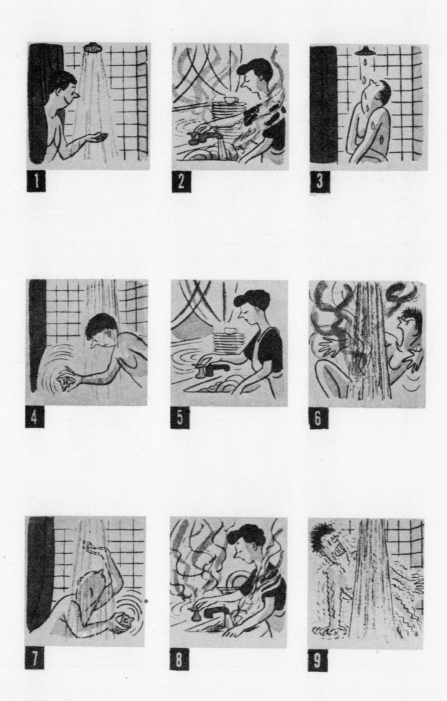

TED KEY

"Let's see if I have it now. Granny wants a double-decker vanilla with caramel nut; no caramel nut, tutti-frutti; no tutti-frutti, walnut pecan; no walnut pecan, chocolate. Grandpa wants a double-decker chocolate with strawberry sherbet; no strawberry sherbet, raspberry sherbet; no raspberry sherbet, orange sherbet; no orange sherbet, banana; no banana, coffee; no coffee, grape; no grape, anything. Mom wants a double-decker chocolate chip; no chocolate chip . . ."

"This route cuts out all of that—I QUOTE—Labor Day traffic."

"Wow—just in time!"

"I hope you were invited"

". . . And to my son, William, *Stop slouch-
ing in your chair, William*, I bequeath . . ."

"Uh-uh."

"Hey, Mom—a chewing-gum mine!"

"You won't see much of Father today, Bruce"

"Glad THIS is over."

" 'Night, dear."